EDITH CA\

JONATHAN EVANS

Front cover: Portrait of Edith Cavell by John Blandy, 2008

First published 2008 by The Royal London Hospital Museum,

Whitechapel, London E1 1BB

(www.bartsandthelondon.nhs.uk/museums)

ISBN 978-0-9517976-5-5

Designed and printed by Metloc Printers

Contents

Acknowledgements

The author gratefully acknowledges the support of Professor John Blandy for his suggestions and help with preparing the text for publication, the choice of illustrations and for his kindness in permitting us to reproduce his portrait of Edith Cavell on the cover. Thanks are also due to Margaret Crispin and Kate Richardson for their comments on the manuscript and to The Royal London Hospital Archives Committee for their support and encouragement. With the exception of the front cover, illustrations are reproduced courtesy of The Royal London Hospital Archives. The author would like to thank The National Archives for permission to quote from the memo by Sir Horace Rowland.

Introduction

Today, Edith Cavell is remembered as a patriot and a heroine of the Great War, through whose efforts upwards of two hundred men were sheltered from capture, many of whom went on to escape from occupied Belgium. In London she is commemorated by a striking monument which stands in St. Martin's Place, adjoining Trafalgar Square and in the shadow of Nelson's Column. There are monuments to her in her native county of Norfolk and in Brussels, her adopted home where she worked and died. A mountain in Canada is named after her. The monument to her in Paris was destroyed by the Nazis in 1940, an indication of the strength of feeling which persisted about her role in the First World War, when her execution in Belgium had led to disquiet around the world. In the nursing profession she is remembered as a pioneer of nursing education, who struggled to establish modern professional nursing and to raise hospital standards in Belgium and worked hard to train nurses who would go on to train others. Perhaps this latter reputation is one with which she would have been content, whilst as a clergyman's daughter and a devout Christian she might have felt shocked about the way her story was manipulated by propagandists in the immediate aftermath of her execution in the autumn of 1915.

An ironic aspect of Edith Cavell's story is that she was someone who respected the German contribution to modern nursing. Like many nurses, she was inspired by the example of Florence Nightingale – who had begun her nursing career in 1851 as a deaconess of Kaiserwerth in Germany. Edith herself first became attracted to the idea of nursing as a career in Bavaria. Far from being a 'little Englander' she spent much of her working life in continental Europe and was a firm believer in international co-operation. Her school of nursing, the Berkendael Institute, was a cosmopolitan one, attracting a number of German nurses as well as those from other European countries, women she expected would go on to teach others. Yet she was prosecuted by a Bavarian and shot by a German firing squad.

Chapter 1. Early life and career as a governess

Edith Cavell was born on December 4 1865, the daughter of the Reverend Frederick Cavell, Vicar of Swardeston, Norfolk, and his wife Louisa Sophia. Edith was the eldest of a family of three daughters and a son. The Cavell family—they pronounced their name to rhyme with travel and not with hell—were originally from Cornwall but had settled near Chelmsford since the sixteenth century. The Reverend Frederick Cavell, who had had previously been the curate of the neighbouring parish of East Carleton, came to Swardeston in 1863 and remained there for 46 years. Frederick Cavell had been born in Holborn, London in about 1825 and had studied at Heidelberg and Kings College, London, where he graduated in theology and was ordained as a priest of the Church of England in 1852. After his ordination, Revd. Cavell worked as a Curate in London. Whilst he was working in London, Frederick Cavell fell in love with his housekeeper's daughter, Miss Louisa Warming, who was ten years younger than him, but the couple delayed their marriage until she had attended a finishing school to acquire the attributes then regarded as necessary for the wife of a clergyman.

The temporary parsonage, an 18th Century building now known as Cavell House, on the south side of the Green in Swardeston, where Edith was born, was vacated within a year of her birth in favour of a new vicarage built at Frederick Cavell's own expense (and costing much more than he could comfortably afford). It was here that the younger Cavell children were born: Florence Mary Scott Cavell, who was no doubt named after the famous nurse Florence Nightingale, was born in 1868; Mary Lillian was born in 1871 and John Frederick was born in 1873. The family did their best to live within their means, but such a large house and their status as gentry obliged them to employ staff to keep up appearances. The domestic staff of the Vicarage was evidently not well paid: a maid in 1876 wrote on her attic bedroom wall the words: 'The pay is small, the food is bad, I wonder why I don't go mad.' Rhymes of this kind were common among Victorian graffiti writers and the words should not be taken too literally. Although money was short in the Cavell household, Edith's early life in Swardeston parsonage was typical of a happy Victorian middle class girl. She grew up in an atmosphere of croquet, tennis, fruit-picking and jam-making with a scholarly father who was not averse to playing bears with his children. In the summer there were visits to the seaside where Edith learned to swim; in winter there was skating, tobogganing and the occasional dance. Above all was the daily work of the vicarage, made busier at weekends with matins, Sunday School and evensong. Frederick Cavell's skills as a preacher were limited and Edith wrote to her cousin, Eddy Cavell: 'Do come and stay again soon, but not for a weekend. Father's sermons are so long and dull'. Eddy Cavell was the youngest of her uncle Edmund's children and was three years older than Edith. She enjoyed his company during the summer holidays which the two Cavell families spent together at Lowestoft.

It has been said of Revd. Frederick Cavell, that he saw life in terms of opportunities for service rather than enjoyment. Sunday lunch was an essential element of family life in the vicarage and an equal amount to that eaten at the table was subsequently distributed amongst the needy of the village. As was customary for a young lady, Edith became accomplished in water-colours, and made many sensitive studies of children, wild flowers and landscapes. Her drawing style in her younger years was not dissimilar to the artist and illustrator of children's books Kate Greenaway (1846–1901) and also resembled those of her contemporary, Beatrix Potter (1866 – 1943). Edith loved animals and the countryside and became an enthusiastic walker. She was, in fact, a thoroughly normal teenager of her class

Swardeston Parish Church

and time; something of a tomboy; of medium height, slender, mad about tennis and not above trying the occasional cigarette (much to the wrath of her father).

Her early education was conducted at home. The family employed a nanny,

Emma Howes in 1871 and ten years later the household included a governess, Harriet Baker. Doubtless Edith's scholarly father saw to some aspects of her education. At the age of 16 Edith was sent her to boarding school, first in St John's Wood in London, later in Clevedon, Bristol, and finally as a pupil-teacher at Laurel Court, Peterborough, in the precinct of the ancient cathedral. This school was run by an unusual person, Margaret Gibson, who had co-founded the school with a Dutch lady, Miss Van Dissell. Laurel Court placed a good deal of emphasis on foreign languages and the Misses Gibson and Van Dissell attracted a high proportion of overseas students to their school. Edith throve as a pupil-teacher: she loved children and they loved her. By this time she had become fluent in French. She had to learn to adjust to Miss Gibson's unusual methods: it was not unknown for her volatile head teacher to throw pupils' belongings out of the window if they failed keep their rooms tidy!

Edith Cavell as a teenager

One of the few vocations open to a young Victorian gentlewoman was that of a governess. It was in that role that Edith went, aged 20 and on the recommendation of Miss Gibson, to the vicarage at Steeple Bumpstead in Essex. The vicar of that parish was Revd. Charles Powell, whose wife was in frail health and largely confined to her bed. The couple had four children and Edith was recruited to take charge of their education. Having herself grown up in a vicarage, she knew all about running one and in view of Mrs. Powell's poor health, Edith took a hand with household management and parish work. She was now an attractive young woman with arresting eyes, and a natural gift for managing children. The young people in her care at this time remembered her fondly as being always full of fun.

At the age of 23 she used a small legacy to travel to the Continent. She visited a free hospital in Bavaria, where she acquired an interest in nursing and medicine. Despite her limited financial means, she donated money to the hospital's funds. She returned to Steeple Bumpsted, but when the Powell children began to grow up and go away to school, it was time for Edith to change her place of employment. She went on to be governess in a series of wealthy families with Quaker connections: the Gurney, the Barclay and the Pryor families. All of these families were deeply involved in charitable works, were active supporters of charity hospitals and were interested in prison reform. They had homes in East Anglia, allowing Edith regular opportunities to visit her parents at Swardeston.

In 1890, on the recommendation of Margaret Gibson, Edith secured her last post as a governess, one that took her abroad for several years. She became governess to the four children of a well-known Belgian lawyer, M. François. The François family lived in a house in the fashionable Rue Louise in Brussels where Edith remained for five years. She was an enthusiastic walker and insisted on walking the children to and from school every morning and afternoon, seldom taking a tram. Whilst she was strict with the children, she never expected them to do anything she was not prepared to do herself and the children admired and respected her. They also found that she was meticulous about their telling the truth at all times. She would get them to perform plays and the children remembered her art lessons, nature rambles and her devotion to pets, dogs in particular. Her favourite author was Charles Dickens and her favourite poets Wordsworth, Longfellow and Tennyson. Summer holidays were spent at the François country retreat near the Dutch

Champs de courses
Watercolour by Edith Cavell, 1893

border, after which Edith would go back to Norfolk. Whilst she was happy in Brussels, Edith gradually became convinced that her career did not lie in the teaching of children. When the François children asked her about her greatest ambition, her reply was curious: 'to be buried in Westminster Abbey.' In 1895 she left her job as governess when she was called home to take care of her father, who was stricken by a sudden illness.

Edith might have married at this time: her second cousin Eddy considered proposing to her. Friends since childhood, it seems not unreasonable to suppose that had he done so she would have accepted him. Sadly, Eddy is said to have told his cousin, Revd. Alexander Cavell that he should never marry because of a nervous disease he had inherited from his mother and which he feared passing on to his children. An attractive woman, there appears to be no evidence of romantic involvement with any other man. By the time Edith's father had recovered from his illness, Edith had made up her mind that nursing was her true vocation. As nursing was largely an all-female profession in her day, she was to spend much of the remainder of her life in the company of other women.

Edith Cavell wearing a necktie
Brussels 1890's

Chapter 2. Training as a nurse

Edith Cavell began her nursing career as an Assistant Nurse at the Fountain Fever Hospital in Tooting, South London. The Fountain had opened in 1893 and was managed by the Metropolitan Asylums Board. The hospital was a makeshift one, but it provided 400 beds for the reception of scarlet fever, smallpox, influenza and other infectious cases from London's sick poor. Edith's application to work there was a daring move: fever nurses who had not previously acquired immunity from deadly communicable diseases, particularly streptococcal diseases such as scarlet fever, erysipelas and pneumococcal pneumonia and diarrhoeal diseases such as typhoid and diphtheria, stood at high risk of catching them and possibly loosing their lives as a result. Edith had been vaccinated against smallpox at the age of 16 and whilst vaccination had greatly reduced the threat that smallpox posed to fever hospital nurses, there was a continuing debate about the communication of the disease, as to whether it spread by aerial infection or from direct personal contact. The dangers of siting fever hospitals in residential neighbourhoods had become apparent and under the Chairmanship of Sir Edmund Hay Currie, the Metropolitan Asylums Board had established an ambulance steamer service to carry patients to riverside hospitals and to hospital ships moored in the lower reaches of the River Thames. This initiative had been successful in helping to isolate fever patients and to reduce the mortality in private houses from smallpox.

Edith applied to the Matron of the Fountain Fever Hospital for an immediate vacancy as an Assistant Nurse, Class II on 6th December 1895, stating in her application: 'I have had no hospital training nor any nursing engagement whatever.' Apart from enquiring about previous nursing experience, the format of the application form gave little opportunity for the applicant to express herself, but enquired about her age (30 in Edith's case), height (5 foot 3 and a half inches), where educated (she wrote 'Kensington') and when she could start work. In response to a question about children, Edith stated that she was unmarried. She gave as her referees Mrs Annette Roberts of Brinton Hall, Norfolk, who had known her since childhood and with whom Edith had stayed for a short time every year and her old employer, Miss Gibson. She advised: 'Either of these ladies will give particulars as to character; as I possess no certificates.' Applicants who wished to become assistant nurses at M.A.B. hospitals were required to provide evidence of character, 'fair education', health and physique, but were not required to hold certificates of previous nurse training. At the Fountain, she was one of forty two Class II assistant nurses and had she stayed for more than a year, could have looked for promotion to Assistant Nurse Class I, and thence to Charge Nurse. Practical instruction in ward work and the nursing of infectious diseases was provided for the assistant nurses by the charge nurses and some lectures were given by the matron and the medical superintendent. It was a condition of service at M.A.B. hospitals that testimonials were granted to all nurses who had satisfactorily completed an engagement of 6 months or longer. After four months at the Fountain, Edith determined to train as a general nurse and on 17th April 1896 she applied for training as a "Non-Paying Probationer" (a salaried student nurse who did not pay her own fees) at the London Hospital, Whitechapel. After a successful interview, and satisfactory references Edith was accepted. The Hospital's preliminary training school was at Tredegar House, Bow Road, and was the brainchild of the London Hospital's Matron of fifteen years standing, Miss Eva Lückes (1853–1919). Edith began her general nurse training there as a pupil in July 1896, shortly before her 31st birthday. Tredegar House had opened a

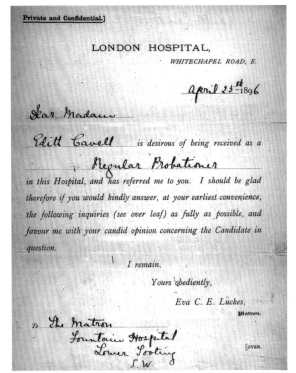

Reference request for Edith Cavell, 1896

year earlier and was the first preliminary nurse training school in England. The school took in up to 32 pupil nurses every 7 weeks.

Miss Lückes was a friend and confidante of Florence Nightingale (1820 – 1910) and shared many of Miss Nightingale's ideas about nursing and her views on the best way to train a nurse. At a time when some hospitals were insisting that new entrants to their nurse training schools should pass an entrance examination, Miss Luckes put more store on her own assessment of applicants' personal qualities at interview and in their references from people with standing in society who were invited to comment upon an applicant's temper and moral character. In Miss Cavell's case, references were supplied by her Matron at the Fountain Hospital, Miss Blackburn, and by Mrs Roberts, who was able to comment on the high tone of Edith's moral character, her pleasing manner, good temper and energetic disposition. Her Matron found her to be 'orderly and methodical and of kindly and gentle disposition' and thought her to be 'a very suitable candidate for training as a hospital nurse.' In late Victorian England, the health of nurses was often put at risk by their

work. Half a century before antibiotics became widely available to help combat infection in hospitals, it was essential for hospital training schools to choose women who were physically fit. On completing her London Hospital application form, Edith was able to give an assurance that, with the exception of a childhood bout of measles, she had always enjoyed robust health. After six months in a fever hospital, Edith was used to a working regime that included long hours and hard work, high standards being expected of her. She had only to

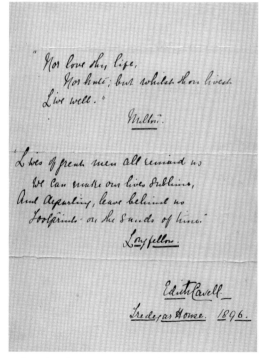

Quotations from Milton and Longfellow recited by Edith Cavell at Tredegar House, July 1896

look at the steadily lengthening lists of names on the memorials in the hospital chapel to be reminded how many nurses and doctors did not survive their training in London's busiest hospital.

At Tredegar House, Edith began her training afresh, learning the elements of anatomy, physiology, hygiene, and nutrition, together with practical sessions on cookery, first aid and the application of bandages and splints. In Miss Lückes' view, however, the primary function of the Preliminary Training School was to impress the candidates with 'a true conception of the work which they are about to enter'. She wished that pupils would come to understand that: 'the noble view of the work is the simple and true one.' Some of the lecture notes that Edith wrote down at this time still survive. These include an introductory lecture on nursing which includes definitions of a medical nurse. To nurse, she wrote, was 'to nourish.' The function of the nurse was 'to help the patient live by aiding nature in the work of recovery'. The nurse's qualities were to include: 'gentleness, patience, tact, cheerfulness, sympathy, order, faithfulness, obedience, power of description and observation.' Eva Lückes, herself the author of popular textbooks on nursing, was fond of writing down favourite quotations and encouraged her pupils to do likewise. It is interesting to note Edith's choice of quotations, which survive in the London Hospital Archives. From the work of the seventeenth century English poet, Milton, she chose: 'Nor love thy life, nor hate, but whilst thou liveth, live well' (John Milton, 1608-74, *Paradise Lost*, Chapter 11) and a prophetic quotation by the nineteenth century American poet, Longfellow: 'Lives of great men all remind us we can make our lives sublime and departing leave behind us footprints in the sands of time.' (Henry Wadsworth Longfellow, 1807-82, *A Psalm of Life*).

The days were long for pupils at Tredegar House, beginning with breakfast at 7 am, followed by prayers and housework before travelling to the hospital for lectures. After lunch, pupils returned to the Tredegar House for practical demonstrations and classes, which carried on into the evening, followed by supper, more prayers and lights out at 10.30 pm. This regime was replicated when Edith began her training in earnest as a regular probationer at the Hospital in Whitechapel on 3rd September 1896. She was now 30 years old and would be regarded as a mature student by the standards of today. At that time, however, the desired age range of probationers entering the hospital's training school was 25 to 36 and the average age of the twelve women in Edith's 'Set' at Tredegar House was 27. Although Edith had seven months hospital experience to supplement her five years teaching in Belgium, some of her set members had done much more nursing. Lizzie Minton, for example had already nursed for over five years. Edith found the routine hard to keep up with:

Miss Eva Lückes, portrait photograph
by Vandyk, London, c. 1900

by February 1898 she had been posted late for breakfast no less than 46 times, more frequently than any other nurse in her Set.

From the day of her arrival at Tredegar House, Edith wore the smart new Probationer's uniform, which had just been introduced: a dress of mauve check cotton with leg of mutton sleeves to the elbow and lower sleeves which were removed to perform nursing tasks, but replaced as soon as the task was completed. Over the dress a white bibbed apron was worn with a plain collar, with matching cuffs at mealtimes, topped off with a simple Sister Dora style cap. The new uniform was said to have been designed by Miss Lückes herself and its introduction coincided with the opening of the Preliminary Training School in 1895. Miss Lückes was determined to enforce strict adherence to the new uniform, which was laundered at high temperature to kill germs and was therefore more hygienic than the clothes which had prevailed at the hospital up to that time.

Training at the London Hospital in those days lasted two years – most teaching was done in the first year whilst in the second the probationer was required to demonstrate what she had learned. The hospital training certificate was awarded after a further two years had elapsed, during which time the nurse worked on the Hospital Staff or on its Private Staff (whose

THE LIFE OF A HOSPITAL NURSE—I.

SKETCHES AT THE LONDON HOSPITAL.

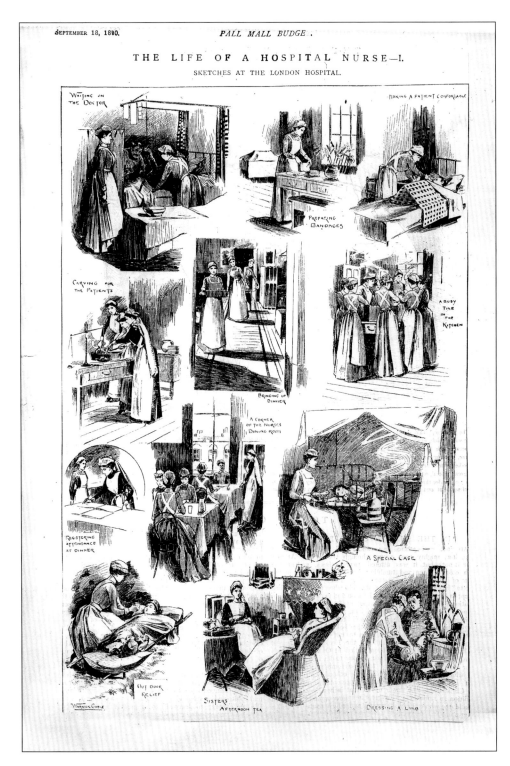

'The life of a hospital nurse' – drawings showing aspects of London Hospital nursing in 1890

nurses worked in private homes), or both. Whilst training, the nurse worked in a variety of different wards and departments, changing from one to another every few weeks. Edith fell ill in early December and was 'warded', that is she was admitted as a patient to one of the wards (this was before the introduction of a separate sick room for nurses). By the end of the year she was back at work and by April 1897 she was working in the Electrical Department at a time when X-rays were beginning to be used at the hospital. X-rays were only discovered, by Röntgen in Germany, in 1895 and the hospital still had little provision of mains electricity. Miss Lückes and her assistants kept a close eye on the progress of the probationers: they recorded pointed, sometimes scathing, remarks about them. In Matron's view, Edith 'was somewhat superficial', her work 'by no means thorough' and she possessed 'a self-sufficient manner, which was very apt to prejudice people against her.' Within the year, however, Edith was able to impress Miss Lückes with the

London Hospital Probationer, possibly Edith Cavell – nursing typhoid patients at Maidstone, c. 1897.

quality of her nursing when she was seconded with a team of nurses to fight the typhoid epidemic in Maidstone, in the autumn and winter of 1897 / 98. Edith worked in the temporary hospital at Padsole School and was on night duty. She and five other nurses from the London lodged with Mrs Josiah Baker. One hundred and thirty people died during the epidemic. The worst was over by December when Edith and the other nurses were rewarded with silver medals from the local population which were presented at a reception attended by the Lord Mayor of London and nine hundred people. After further training at the London and an examination in which she achieved a 'very satisfactory' mark, Edith qualified for her certificate of training in September 1898. Even so Miss Lückes' appraisal of her was cool: 'Edith Cavell had plenty of capability for her work when she chooses to exert herself, but she was not very much in earnest, not at all punctual, and not a nurse that could altogether be depended upon.'

In October 1898, Miss Lückes assigned Edith to the London Hospital Private Nursing Staff. Matron liked to select nurses she thought would fit well into any social setting for her Private Staff. The London's Private Nursing Institution had been founded in 1886 and comprised a staff of over 200 trained nurses who were engaged to nurse patients in their own homes. The fees charged for their services, which ranged upwards from six guineas a week, were valued by the Hospital's management as an important source of income to the Charity. The Hospital's Chairman, The Hon. Sydney Holland, afterwards Viscount Knutsford, also perceived that the private staff helped to keep the Charity in the public eye. Hospital consultants, when attending their private patients, found it convenient to work with nurses versed in the latest hospital methods and capable of setting up an operation room in a private house. The patients and their families valued the services of reliable, trained nurses, particularly when their relative wealth and social circumstances prohibited them from admission to charity hospitals like the London. In the years before the First World War, an average of 50 calls a day had to be refused by the Institution because all the private staff nurses were already placed.

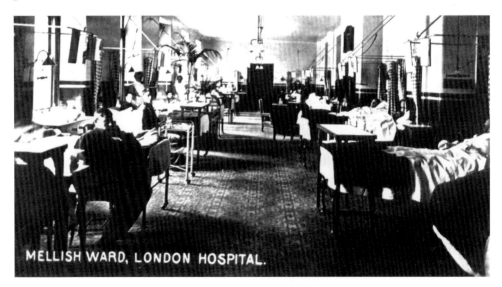

MELLISH WARD, LONDON HOSPITAL.

Mellish Ward, London Hospital, 1905

With her training in fever nursing and her experience at Maidstone, she was chosen to go to West Norwood to nurse a boy of 14 with typhoid. Edith nursed him for 12 weeks until he had recovered. During her period on the Private Staff, Edith wrote to Matron at weekly intervals, knowing that Miss Lückes expected to be kept informed about the progress of her cases. Her private cases included patients with cancer, appendicitis, and pneumonia. On the last day of the 19th Century, Edith transferred to the Hospital Staff: she was appointed Staff Nurse in Mellish ward, a men's surgical ward which took in emergency cases on a daily basis. As a day nurse, Edith was required to be on duty in the ward from 7 o'clock in the morning until 9.30 in the evening with 3 hours off duty allowed daily before 6.00pm. Her salary for her first year was £24 with a small allowance for washing.

As Nurse Mellish she gained valuable experience. The ward sister for the previous two years had been Ethel Hope Beecher, a gifted nurse and ward manager from an old military family who volunteered to be one of the half dozen London Hospital nurses the Princess of Wales (later Queen Alexandra) sent to South Africa where the Second Boer War had broken out. Miss Beecher sailed for South Africa on Christmas Day 1899. She insisted on taking with her Edith's predecessor as Staff Nurse Mellish, Miss Clara Evans. Within five months of sailing Miss Evans was dead of dysentery, which she contracted when nursing at Bloemfontein. Miss Beecher went on to become Matron-in Chief of Queen Alexandra's Imperial Nursing Service. Miss Lückes, whilst acknowledging Miss Beecher's gifts as a ward manager, was inclined to think that the comfort and happiness of the patients in Mellish Ward had been sometimes sacrificed to make the ward look smart.

The same regime perpetuated under Miss Beecher's successor as ward sister, Miss Lillian Gough, who was appointed Sister Mellish seven weeks after Edith had taken up post as staff nurse. They had a difficult working relationship and Edith became convinced Miss Gough had taken against her. The smart appearance of her ward and the technical side of her work were praised by Matron, but Miss Gough's manner with her probationers left much to be desired. This did not endear Sister to her staff nurse, Miss Cavell, to whom the careful management and teaching of trainees was an essential element of nursing. Matron got to hear of Miss Gough's and Miss Cavell's disagreements. Whilst she privately felt that Edith's qualms about her ward sister's methods may have been justified, she felt obliged to back the senior nurse. By this time, Miss Lückes had revised her earlier assessment of Edith to the extent that she now held her to be a conscientious nurse, 'steady and nice minded,' but Matron still felt that Miss Cavell could improve her work by being more methodical and that she was inclined to over estimate her own abilities. Had she been happier in her ward, Edith would have remained at The London. Her friend, a clever, business-like and well-educated nurse named Eveline Dickinson had been promoted to Sister in the newly-opened Finsen Light Department, where patients were treated with ultra violet light for lupus, a tuberculous, ulcerative disease of the skin. Like Miss Cavell, Miss Dickinson was a clergyman's daughter: her father was the Vicar of Bodmin in Cornwall. Matron thought her conceited but efficient. Had Edith stuck to her post she would very likely have succeeded Lillian Gough as Sister Mellish when Miss Gough became ill and left the hospital staff a few months later. In the event, however, Edith intimated to Miss Lückes that she would be willing to accept a post as Night Superintendent at St Pancras Infirmary, where the Matron was Miss Ellen Moir, a former London Hospital Sister. She left the London Hospital to take up her new appointment at St. Pancras Infirmary on 3rd January 1901.

Chapter 3. Nursing under the Poor Law

St. Pancras Infirmary, in Dartmouth Park Hill, North London, had been completed in 1885 and was managed under the Poor Law by the St. Pancras Board of Guardians. With a medical staff of only three doctors to care for nearly 500 patients and no clinical teaching, it was very different from the teaching hospital atmosphere to which Edith had become used at the London. The Infirmary had opened a school of nursing in 1890, but as one of two night

Portrait photograph of Edith Cavell as Night Superintendent, St. Pancras Infirmary c. 1901

superintendents Edith spent the next three years on night duty, where her opportunities for teaching probationers were necessarily limited. Many of the patients were elderly and chronically sick, with diseases such as pulmonary tuberculosis and bronchitis. Many of the patients at the Infirmary were referred by nearby voluntary hospitals like the University College and the Royal Free Hospitals, whose by-laws prohibited the admission of incurables. Some patients were destitute: of those who did not die in the infirmary, many were discharged to the local workhouse or were maintained at home under a system known as 'outdoor relief'. The nights were long and arduous: Edith and the other Night Superintendent, Miss Emma Berridge, formerly of the London's Private Staff, each had charge of 250 beds. Miss Berridge had been born in Queensland, Australia in 1863. Edith's sister, Florence Cavell, who had also trained as a nurse, had taken a post as a Night Superintendent of an infirmary in Hendon, north west of London and she and Edith would doubtless have met up during their time off duty. Meanwhile, Edith tried without success to obtain a posting elsewhere.

Eventually, in November 1903, she was appointed as Assistant Matron at Shoreditch Infirmary, a former workhouse in Hoxton Street, which later became St Leonard's Hospital. Once again the Matron was an old Londoner, Miss Joanna Inglis (1855 – 1958), who had held the post for four years. Miss Inglis worked closely with Edith and came to like and admire her, but later wrote that she never felt close to her. Hoxton was notorious as one of the least savoury parts of London: the social commentator Charles Booth characterised some of its streets as being habituated by semi-criminals. Shoreditch Infirmary served a local population of 130,000 crammed into an area of less than a square mile. As at St. Pancras, the quality of care in the

Infirmary rested more on the nursing than on the small number of medical staff. There were 120 nurses, many training at its school of nursing, which had been running since 1889. At Shoreditch, Edith had charge of much of the supervision of the wards as well as the laundry and the linen room. She also found time to develop her natural gift for teaching. She was, however, restless and made numerous unsuccessful applications for Matrons' posts in more congenial places, such as Tavistock in Devon, Ventnor on the Isle of Wight and Swansea in South Wales.

Before the First World War it was quite usual for nurses to wear uniform when off-duty. Here, Edith Cavell wears her uniform as Assistant Matron, Shoreditch Infirmary when visiting family or friends, c. 1905

By January 1906 Edith had become thoroughly exhausted. Apart for a brief holiday in Cornwall in June 1902, she had been nursing for ten years without a break. She needed a long rest and a change of air. She resigned her post at Shoreditch when, in the Spring of 1906 her old friend Eveline Dickinson, who was to marry and move to Ireland that September, asked Edith go on holiday with her. On leaving Shoreditch Infirmary she was presented with a sapphire and pearl pendant by her probationers and staff colleagues. After her death, she was to be commemorated by an inscription in the old Workhouse Hall at Shoreditch, which was re-named St. Leonard's Hospital in 1920. Feeling better after her long and pleasant holiday, Edith returned to Swardeston Vicarage, from where she endeavoured to find a Matron's position. Miss Lückes was willing to help her get fresh work, but competition for the better salaried posts was fiercer than ever and she did not meet with initial success. Eventually, she found a job in Manchester, first as a Queen's District Nurse and then in the Queen's District Home at Ashton New Road, where she deputised for the Matron, Miss Hall, who was seriously ill. The Queen's District Home was smaller than the other hospitals in which she had worked, but Edith found the experience valuable as it taught her how to run a hospital on a slender budget. In Manchester, as at Shoreditch, Edith proved herself a capable teacher, able to illustrate her lectures with her own diagrams. She wrote to

Drawing of a street scene, possibly Norwich, by Edith Cavell, c. 1902

Miss Lückes on 12th March 1907 seeking help in finding trained nurses willing to fill a temporary engagement for 3 months. It was an anxious time for Edith as she had to nurse Miss Hall as well as managing the home, which involved 'much book keeping.'

Chapter 4. Return to Brussels

In 1907 Edith Cavell was aged 41 and was beginning to despair of finding promotion in British hospitals. Then came her chance. Through her contact with the François family for whom she had worked in Brussels, she was brought to the attention of Dr Antoine Depage, a leading Belgian surgeon, when she took a temporary post nursing a child who was under his care. Antoine Depage, (1862 – 1919) had qualified in 1887 and two years later founded a research laboratory, to serve the hospitals of the Brussels area. He became a prominent campaigner for the improvement of standards of medical care in the area, assisted in this work by Marie Picard, whom he married in 1893, and who became his secretary. In particular, Depage was anxious to challenge what he saw as the poor clinical practice of the religious orders which ran many of the hospitals in Belgium. In 1907, with the help of his wife and their wealthy and influential friends, Depage was able to found a training school for nurses, where he hoped the best standards would be taught. A gifted surgeon himself, he appreciated the considerable progress that surgery had made during the second half of the Nineteenth Century through the introduction of anaesthetics, antisepsis and (latterly) asepsis - whereby surgical operations could be made much safer through the use of sterile instruments, dressings and equipment. In Britain, the teaching hospitals had kept pace with these developments and so had those nurses who, like Edith, had trained in their nurse training schools. Depage wanted nurses in Belgium to be trained in similar methods and to raise the standards of the lay nurses (known as infirmières) of the day who were often unable to keep themselves clean, let alone the wards in which they worked. The President of Dr Depage's Ladies' Committee happened to be the mother-in-law of Edith's former pupil Marguerite François and it was she who told him about the family's former English governess, now a trained nurse, who had held positions of responsibility in several hospitals and spoke fluent French.

Edith was quick to accept the post in Brussels when it was offered to her. To set up a school of nursing from scratch was hard work. She felt it was important to begin with just a few pupils at first and to select educated women as she intended them to become nurse teachers themselves. Within a week of her arrival at the new school, which was converted from four adjoining houses in the Rue de la Culture in the Ixelles district of Brussels, Edith was writing to her former Matron, Eva Lückes, hoping to enlist her support. Miss Luckes was keen to help. Whilst she was not active in the International Congress of Nurses, unlike her contemporary and rival, Ethel Gordon Manson (Mrs Bedford Fenwick), Miss Lückes was proud of her "Old Londoners" who held positions of responsibility in hospitals all over the world. She maintained a regular correspondence with them, entered the details into what she termed her 'supplementary register' and circulated information about appointments held by former London Hospital nurses in her 'Matron's annual letter.'

Miss Cavell had to persuade her governing committee of the necessity of hospital arrangements she had taken for granted in England, such as the nursing of patients at night. She planned for her probationers to sign contracts to work for her for five years: three years' training followed by two more years' private nursing or institute nursing in the service of the school. The name of her school was the École Belge D' Infirmières Diplômées (the Belgian School of Certificated Nurses). As an Englishwoman and a Protestant her task was especially difficult since nursing in Belgium had hitherto been the virtual monopoly of the Roman Catholic religious sisterhoods. She had to use all her charm and tact to try to overcome the prejudices of staff and patients in a country where the nursing profession had been held in low esteem. Indeed, the Belgian public's perception of nurses was not unlike that which had prevailed in England half a century earlier: that it was not a suitable profession for cultivated and educated ladies.

She began in October 1907 with just five probationers. One of them, Mlle Clara Boehme (afterwards Mrs Stanton) recalled her first encounter with her new Matron:

'I arrived and at once was shown into Miss Cavell's study where she was seated at her desk, wearing a dress of soft dark blue material relieved at the neck by a starched white collar. Her dark brown hair, slightly grey at the temples, was neatly arranged and parted. Her clear grey eyes were direct and searching in their gaze.

Her voice was low, agreeable and cultured; her French fluent. I was at once attracted by her, and it was during this first interview that I formed the impression (which never left me) that everything around Edith Cavell, the atmosphere of her room, the neatness of her attire, her attitude and poise, the words she used, all conveyed her characteristic efficiency, thoroughness, serenity and kindness.'

She devised a uniform for her probationers and it is a measure of the enduring influence Miss Lückes had upon Edith that she based it in large part upon on that at the London. The main difference between the two uniforms, both of which were billowy and had puff sleeves, was that the probationers in Edith's school wore dresses of the same soft, mid blue colour that was reserved for sisters at her old teaching hospital. As a probationer and a staff nurse, Edith had worn mauve dresses and had had never succeeded in coming 'out in blue', the term used by nurses at London for being promoted to sister. She had thus been denied the opportunities for gracious living which sisters at the hospital enjoyed during the Edwardian period. The first four probationers received daily teaching (except on Sundays) from Miss Cavell on anatomy, physiology, hygiene, the principal internal diseases, elementary pharmacology and general nursing; additional lectures were given by a junior doctor. Edith planned to extend the curriculum of her school to include new techniques, such as culturing for microbes associated with particular diseases [bacteriology] and testing urine.

Group photograph featuring Dr. Antoine Depage, Edith Cavell, staff and probationers at the training school for nurses, rue de la Culture, Brussels

She wrote to the British journal, *The Nursing Mirror*, about her new regime:

'The contrast the probationers present to the nuns in their heavy stiff robes, and the lay nurses in their grimy apparel, is the contrast of the unhygienic past with the enlightened present. These Belgian probationers in three years time will look back on the first days of trial with wonder.'

In time more of the teaching fell to others, like Professor Hegér, Dr le Boeuf, Dr Mahillon and Dr Mayer, while Edith lectured on what she termed 'the art of the infirmière' (the theory and practice of nursing).

As Edith later remembered: 'for Belgium, everything about the profession was new.' A whole new terminology had to be introduced. Terms like "on duty" and "off duty" were not in current use in Belgium. Doctors in Belgium were unused to being assisted by nurses at operations. Nuns in Belgian hospitals did not normally wash patients – such work was left to servants - patients and staff at the school had to get used to patients being given bed baths by nurses. Patients' friends and relatives were a worry for Edith as they tended to wander off to the kitchen and come back with bowls of soup and other foods or order patients' meals for them, sometimes in contravention of the diet ordered by the doctor. Water for surgical use had to be sterilized by boiling in kitchen saucepans.

Edith asked Miss Lückes to recommend a nurse, one who spoke French 'fairly well' to take up a senior position in Dr Depage's Surgical Institute. The Institute was equipped with what Edith termed 'two beautiful [operating] theatres,' and had been built in Place Georges, near to the School of Nursing, opening in November 1907. Miss Lina Maude of the London Hospital's Private Nursing Staff was recommended and duly engaged. Unlike Edith, who was a natural linguist and familiar with Belgian manners and customs, Miss Maud, in common with some other British nurses who came to Brussels at this time, found her knowledge of French language severely tested and the adjustment to life and work in Belgium difficult. Miss Helen Graham, formerly a ward sister at the London Hospital, became a sister in Edith's School in January 1908 and proved to be a great help. Within a few months, however, Miss Graham left to be married. By April there were thirteen probationers in the school and Edith was feeling confident enough to write a report for publication in *The Nursing Mirror* about her institution and its teething troubles. Indeed, by the end of that year, she was making sufficiently good progress to be able to recommend her assistant, Miss Irene Evans, (another Old Londoner), as superintendent of the lay nurses in the Hospital of St Jean, a large hospital in Rue de Marais in Brussels. Whilst she was pleased that her nurses were making professional progress, these appointments meant that Edith was in need of trained assistants herself. Later she was to regret that, like Miss Maude, Miss Evans suffered in her new appointment as a result of the narrow-mindedness of others and from malicious gossip.

Chapter 5. Berkendael Institute

Edith found the work ethos of some of her probationers frustratingly different from her own, particularly that of some of those from more affluent families. It was important for her to instil a sense of pride and compatriotism among her probationers, drawn as they were from several different European countries and from a variety of social backgrounds. She had to convince them of the importance of punctuality and hard work. Edith expected her probationers to work hard, especially during the first three months when they had to show that they were tough enough to be nurses and could clean floors and dust the wards. This was unsettling for those who had grown up in homes where this type of work was done by domestic servants. When the mother of one such probationer wrote to Miss Cavell about her daughter's problems, Edith replied:

'Such difficulties are unavoidable with all young girls of the wealthier class until they come to recognize that the work is not a social stigma. … I hope that in time the several excellent foreign students here will encourage the Belgian girls themselves to set an example which will promote and popularise the nursing profession.'

When she began to send her trained nurses out to work with private patients and with Belgian doctors, they were not, at first, given sufficient respect, but were treated as servants by some of the families who hired them. Doctors, unused to working with trained nurses, were sometimes overly familiar with them. It took time for professional interaction between doctors and nurses to develop, but gradually more doctors began to use the Clinique, as the buildings in the Rue de la Culture came to be known. Gradually, the young Belgian pupils took to their Matron, or Directrice as she was termed, and they began to appreciate her quiet sense of humour. Edith's own indoor uniform consisted of a blue serge woollen dress, a plain collar and a Sister Dora cap. She wore her uniform under a long blue coat when going out. This contrasted with the working attire favoured by her mentor, Miss Lückes, who wore elaborate silk dresses, fine lace caps and jewellery. Edith's regime at the Institute was strict: nurses were discouraged from fraternising with one another during the early months of their training and she urged her probationers to have commitment to nursing their patients. A draft (in French) of a letter Edith wrote in July 1909 to a grateful patient, who had given a present to Nurse Birch, reveals her policy on the propriety of such matters. A translation reads:

'I thank you for your kindness in sending a present to Nurse Birch. I regret that it is not allowed for nurses to accept them. You will forgive me if I send you a Postal Order for 17 francs.'

Edith's influence spread to other hospitals in Brussels. By 1909, a year in which twenty three new probationers enrolled at her school, (now sometimes known by the rather grand title of the 'Intsitut de Berkendael'), Miss Cavell's establishment had a rival. Another school of nursing, the School of Sainte-Camille was founded. The

Edith Cavell's appeal to Belgian women considering nursing as a career.

following year, the Department of Hospitals of the City of Brussels opened an additional school.

July 1909 saw Edith presenting a report on the nursing situation in Belgium to the second Quinquennial Congress of the International Congress of Nurses, meeting in London. She was part of a Belgian 'fraternal delegation' which attended the Congress. The welcoming address was given by Mrs. Bedford Fenwick (1857 – 1947) and the new president of the Congress, elected at the meeting, was Agnes Karll, (1868 – 1927), President of the Association of Professional Nurses in Germany and founder of the College of Women in Leipzig, where a two year basic nurse training course was taught. Like Mrs. Fenwick, Fraulein Karll was an eloquent supporter of state registration for nurses. However, Congress delegates from Sweden and

Holland declared themselves opposed to registration, stating that nursing in their countries was not yet ready for legislation. The Hon. Sydney Holland, Chairman of the London Hospital, spoke from the floor of the meeting to point out that 232 hospital matrons in Britain had signed a petition opposing registration. Mr Holland's remarks were not well-received and the Congress passed a resolution pressing for statutory registration in all countries 'both in the interests of the professional status of trained nurses and of the public they serve.' The Congress also passed a resolution in favour of women's suffrage and some speakers, such as R.B. Haldane, Secretary of State for War, found themselves being frequently interrupted by suffragettes. At the end of the Congress there was a banquet attended by 300 nurses from 17 countries – Edith was very probably one of them. Fraternal delegates and visitors also enjoyed a visit to Windsor Castle at the personal invitation of King Edward VII and a reception at the American Embassy in London.

Training Certificate signed by Edith Cavell, 1915

It was, perhaps, fired with the spirit of internationalism that Edith wrote an appeal to Belgian women to consider a career in nursing:

'Do you dislike the career of a nurse? Are you too well educated, too well born to stoop so low? Nay, rather raise the work to the heights to which it is capable of being carried - Your sisters in Denmark, Germany, Holland, America, England have made it a great and honourable profession; they have given their noblest and best; they have not only spent their money and their influence, but their whole lives in the great service of humanity. They have found in it the means of the widest social reform, the purest philanthropy, the truest humanity – they have made themselves the handmaids of that science which not only assuages, heals and delivers the suffering of today, but reaches on through ever widening circles to the dawn of perfect manhood when disease shall be unknown.'

In October 1910 the first training certificates were awarded to two of Miss Cavell's original probationers: each was given a training school badge which Edith had designed herself. The central motif of the badge was an edelweiss flower of a pale blue background encircled with the words: 'ECOLE BELGE D' 'INFIRMIERES DIPLOMEES'. The choice of the edelweiss as a symbol of the school was deliberate: a perennial alpine plant belonging to the daisy family, with a white, star-shaped flower, it struggles to establish itself in the high mountains of Europe – an allusion to Miss Cavell's aspirations for her nurses. The badge is surprisingly modern in its design. The training certificate, or Dilpome de capacité, was also probably designed by Edith herself. It testified

Photograph of Sister Wilkins
with Edith's dog, Jack

that the nurse had served for three years at the Ecole Belge d'Infirmières Diplomées and associated medical establishments and had satisfactorily completed the required courses of study satisfied the examiners from the point of view of their conduct, good character, morality and their care of the sick. Each was signed by Edith, as Directrice, by the President of the School Council and also by the various teachers of anatomy, physiology, pathology

Registration of nurses was introduced in Belgium in 1910. At the time, this appeared to be a bold move - state registration was not introduced in England until 1919 - but Miss Cavell was not convinced. She commented:

'A certificate is now given by the State to

all women who have passed their examination, but it can be obtained merely by attending a prescribed course of lectures for one year. This shows the completely erroneous idea of nursing still held in this country.'

That year also saw the opening of a large new publicly funded hospital in Brussels, the Hospital of St. Gilles. The governing authorities asked Miss Cavell to provide the nursing staff of the new hospital and to become its effective matron. Henceforth, Miss Cavell's school could make use of St. Gilles Hospital to

Edith Cavell, photographed with her dog 'Jack', c. 1915

provide the clinical setting for much of its practical nurse training. Whilst the new hospital bore similarities in terms of its management and funding to the Poor Law infirmaries where Edith had worked in England, the clinical facilities at St. Gilles were much better than those at St. Pancras and Shoreditch infirmaries. At St. Gilles, her nurses encountered many cases of dropsy (oedema of the abdomen, often treated by inserting a drainage tube) and diphtheria (where an emergency tracheotomy might have to be performed to maintain an airway and prevent a child from dying from suffocation). Traditional remedies such as blood letting by dry and wet cupping, the application of leeches and the administration of alcohol as a stimulant were practiced alongside newer treatments like lumbar punctures, saline infusions and drug therapies.

By 1912 Edith had thirty two students in training and her pupils were staffing three hospitals, three private nursing-homes and a number of schools and kindergartens. Within a year plans were going ahead to build a new, larger hospital. At the beginning of 1914, her institute consisted of over ninety students and staff of many nationalities, including Germans. Sister Whitlock recorded that Miss Cavell had a special regard for her Belgian pupils, whose country she had adopted and loved as her own. By this time she superintended a variety of organisations: hospitals, clinics and a private nursing institution. Her private patients included Grace Jemmett, daughter of friends of Edith's sister, Lillian, and her husband, Longworth Wainwright. Dr Wainwright had recommended that Grace be sent to Brussels after she became addicted to morphine in the course of treatment for a serious illness. 'Gracie' remained for five years or so and accompanied Edith when she returned to England on holiday. They sometimes stayed with a young family named Harrison who had a cottage at West Runton, a seaside village in Norfolk, sometimes with Edith's mother. Edith eventually came to treat the girl almost as a daughter, but Grace was demanding of her time and as a drug addict she had to be carefully watched.

Edith was also fond of her two dogs, Don and Jack, both born in 1909 and she even wrote a booklet about keeping dogs. It included advice on kennel design (with a sketch of a kennel made out of a barrel), together with remarks on feeding, exercise, grooming and training. She held that a good watch dog, which could distinguish between friends and foes, could be cultivated by making him a companion and putting the animal on a chain only when absolutely necessary. Both dogs were fiercely protective of her and Jack in particular is said to have bitten anyone who dared look at his mistress. Some of Miss Cavell's probationers at this time, like Jacqueline Van Til and Ruth Moore (Mrs Hellyer) later published reminiscences. Their impression of Edith is of someone very dedicated to her work, someone who would never shrink from doing herself what she asked of others and who kept a watchful eye on her students and staff. Mlle. van Til recalled nurses of all nationalities having to speak French when on duty and being warned for raising their voices or for lapses of good manners. Three times a day Matron would walk to the institutions where her nurses were placed, accompanied by her dogs. Ruth Moore remembered that Miss Cavell, during her daily ward inspections, would run a finger over surfaces, both high and low, checking for a speck of dust. She also recalled her enjoyment of Miss Cavell's lectures on the theory and practice of nursing. Both nurses remembered that they never dared to be late for meals: that Matron would time their time of arrival at the breakfast table and deprive latecomers of their off duty time. This sounds surprising in view of Edith's frequent lateness at mealtimes during her own training, but is perhaps indicative of someone who disliked seeing her own perceived faults manifested in others: an all too human failing. Whist Matron might be informed of her nurses' errors, she was usually willing to give them the opportunity to make amends and dismissals were rare

By 1912, the success of Miss Cavell's school of nursing meant that the cramped and inconvenient premises of the Clinique in the Rue de la Culture were fast becoming untenable. Mme. Ernest Solvay stepped in with an offer to match any money collected for new premises. Plans for a new Institute were drawn up. A site for a new hospital and training school was chosen in the rue de Bruxelles (afterwards rue Edith Cavell) and building commenced the following year. The private nursing aspect of the Berkendael Institute's work had grown. Lillian Waterer, a member of the London Hospital Private Nursing Staff, who was sent by Miss Lückes to help out at the Berkendael in November 1912 later recalled:

'There was a fairly large staff of private nurses of mixed nationalities, even a large sized Russian girl and one morning the day Sister told me that Miss Cavell was worried because they needed a Visiting Nurse and they were all out. So I went to Miss Cavell and offered to take the case. To the fact that I had just done twelve hours night duty she never gave a thought. Why should she? It was just what she would do herself and I was a 'Londoner'.'

Miss Waterer had found that most of the treatments given at the Berkendael consisted of simple dressings and fomentations (local applications of hot and cold, given alternately to treat inflammations).

Edith wrote to Miss Lückes in April 1913 – her first letter for some time – informing her that 'the work is still very arduous and trying. The spirit of the people is so opposed to the spirit of nursing. The young girls are brought up with no idea of duty and are selfish and too fond of pleasures.' She was 'grieved 'by the harsh treatment afforded to Miss Lina Maud and Miss Irene Evans, the 'old Londoner' sisters she had recommended for senior positions in Brussels. Both had been made the subject of 'slanderous gossip' and had been 'sacrificed to the critical and narrow ideas of the people among whom they worked' and by 1913, whilst their efforts were greatly valued by Edith, both had left their posts. On a happier note, Edith could report that:

'"the trained nurse" is making progress, all the new nursing homes and hospitals are engaging lay nurses and we have more demands than we can supply'. Recruitment of Belgian candidates for the school was slower than she would have desired and half of the pupils were foreigners. However she had 'all the board schools under our supervision and 12 nurses at work in them.' She was also happy to report progress in Belgium's hospitals 'from the point of view of good order, cleanliness and good nursing' and looked forward to the opening of a new School of Nursing in two years' time. Having built up a good working relationship with the governing body of the Berkendael Institute, Edith felt able to advise Miss Lückes:

'My Council are very good and kind, and I always feel now that I have their support in any difficulty. They have the work very much at heart, and have raised the necessary funds to build us a new school which will be worthy of the object. We hope to be installed in about two years.'

A happy event which occurred in 1913 was the return of one of Edith's original probationers, Clara Boehme, now Mrs Stanton, to the Clinique, for her confinement. Clara's baby, Annie Stanton, was the first child to be born there.

Edith's father died in 1910 and Edith would have liked her widowed mother to move to Brussels to live with her. Eventually, just before Christmas 1913, Mrs Cavell arrived for a trial stay in Brussels. It was not a success: she found it difficult to adapt to living abroad and did not get along with Grace Jemmett. Early in the New Year Mrs. Cavell returned to England.

Chapter 6. Belgium Invaded

The hot, high summer of 1914 saw Edith in Norfolk, staying in her mother's house in College Road, Norwich and at the Harrison's cottage at West Runton. On 28 June, just before she left Brussels, the Archduke Franz Ferdinand of Austria and his wife Sophie, Duchess of Hoenberg, had been assassinated at Sarajevo by supposedly pro-Serbian nationalists, an event which was ultimately to lead Austria-Hungary to declare war on Serbia (which was allied to Russia). Under the terms of the Triple Alliance, 1882 (between Austria-Hungary, Germany and Italy) and the Secret Treaty of 1892 (between Russia and France) and the intricate and virtually irreversible plans for the mobilization of their armed forces, within weeks all the European great powers, except Italy, had gone to war. Germany declared war on France on 3rd August 1914, one day after issuing an ultimatum to Belgium demanding the right of German troops to pass through as part of planned attack on France. The German army invaded Belgium on 3rd August, which lead Britain to declare war on Germany for violating Belgian neutrality.

Sister White, left in charge at the Berkendael, sent Edith an urgent telegram on 1st August and she hurried back to Brussels from her holiday. Her first problem was to deal with, the repatriation of her six trainee German nurses. Her next care was to lay in equipment and provisions for the expected wounded. By August 20 she was acting as War Correspondent to *The Nursing Mirror* and recorded the entry, that day, of the invading German troops into Brussels. The Belgian capital city was spared from widespread destruction by the decision of the King to declare it an open city, whereupon the home guard who had been charged with its defence were evacuated. Her description was concise and yet moving:

'In the evening word came that the enemy were at the gates. At midnight bugles were blowing bugles summoning the civic guard to lay down their arms and leave the city.' The following day 'with much pomp and circumstance of war, the German troops marched into Brussels and the Town Hall, where the brave [Belgian] tricolour came down and the German stripes of black white and red took its place … I am a looker on after all, for it is not my country whose soil is desecrated and whose sacred places are laid waste. I can only feel the deep and tender pity of a friend within the gates and observe with sympathy and admiration the high courage and self control of a people enduring a long and terrible agony.'

The German occupation of Belgium was marked by a deliberate display of frightfulness designed to intimidate the Belgians in order to secure maximum civilian co-operation. This included massacres of civilians at Dinant and in Louvain, where for five consecutive days the city was burnt and looted. Its library of ancient manuscripts was destroyed, along with its university, churches and many other public buildings. The Battle of Dinant on 15th August 1914 had seen many Belgian troops become separated from their units and taking cover in woodland nearby. On 23rd August the First Battle of Mons began, from which the British Expeditionary Force and the French Army made a fighting retreat, losing many prisoners in the process.

At first Edith had little to do at the Berkendael. Having helped to arrange for her German and Dutch nurses to return to their homelands, she saw to the departure of some of her British nurses. In September 1914 she could have returned to England with seventy other nurses, who had been given permission to leave Belgium thanks to the intervention of the United States Minister in Brussels. She chose to remain in post, tending Belgian and German wounded in the Red Cross ambulance which she had fitted up. Edith suggested that Grace Jemmett and the sisters on her staff return home, but they could not be persuaded to leave. The Germans might have interned Edith as an enemy alien, but instead she was allowed to remain at liberty. Money was in short supply at the Clinique, where half the beds were empty and whilst work on building a new training school still went on, it progressed only slowly. Many wards at the hospital at St. Gilles were also closed as the local authority could not afford to keep them open and because many nurses were away nursing war wounded.

Chapter 7. Escape network

At the beginning of November 1914, two British soldiers, dressed in civilian clothes, arrived at the hospital. Both had been severely wounded at Mons. They were Colonel Dudley Boger, who had commanded the Cheshire Regiment, and Sergeant Frederick Meachin. They were being helped by Herman Capiau, a mining engineer, who was a friend of Albert Libiez, a Mons barrister and journalist, who had been hiding the fugitives for several weeks. Capiau brought Boger and Meachin to the Clinique, hearing that it was run by an Englishwoman. Edith took them in, treated their wounds and before long sent them both on their way back to England via Holland. Colonel Boger was caught and sent to a prisoner-of-war camp, but Sergeant Meachin arrived home safely, after several narrow escapes. Two weeks later came the first of ten French soldiers, who had become detached from their units after the Battle of Charleroi. Over the course of the next two months Edith managed to send all ten men, one by one, across the frontier to Holland. As the weeks passed, other escaped soldiers found their way to the Clinique. At Christmas, Edith found herself hosting a children's party. She was managing a hospital whose in-patients included several wounded Germans while English servicemen were hidden in the cellar below. At the Christmas party, an English clergyman, Stirling Gahan noted that 'Nurse Cavell moved pleasantly among her guests, and there, to our great amusement and delight, were a couple of British "tommies".'

Near the battlefield of Mons lay the ancient castle of Bellignies, seat of the de Croÿ family, which had been converted into a Red Cross hospital under the care of Princesse Marie, who received wounded from both sides indiscriminately. Before long the de Croÿs were also taking in allied fugitives who had been hiding in the nearby Forest of Mormal. The Princesse de Croÿ proved to be a clever photographer, and was soon in demand to supply fake passports. She got in touch with Edith Cavell, and over the next few months an escape network had been set up whose password was 'Yorc'—the reverse of Croÿ. Sometimes Edith took her own photographs. Sometimes she used the old ruse of tearing a card in half to afford identification. Escapes were noted as 'operations' in the theatre book. Eventually she was to get about two hundred away.

On 11th March 1915 she wrote to her cousin Eddy (Edmund Cavell jnr.), who had written to offer his help, enclosing a list of soldiers that she was eager to have news about. She claimed that the men were 'relations of some of the girls here' but they were more likely people she had helped to escape. She told him there were insufficient numbers of patients to keep them busy, but incautiously admitted that: '…there are other things to do and I am helping in ways I may not describe here.' She ended her letter in a nostalgic and affectionate tone:

' I like to look back on the days when we were young and life was fresh and beautiful and the country so desirable and sweet.

Many thanks for your kind letter, my dear Cousin, from

Yours affectionately,

Edith'

Photograph of Edith Cavell in civilian dress which featured on her identity papers, 1915

As early as August 1914, Edith had indicated in a letter to her mother that she was keeping a written record of her experiences in occupied Belgium. Half a dozen pages of the diary that she kept survived the War and were discovered thirty years later stuffed into a cushion. The cushion was among the possessions which were recovered by Edith's sisters, Florence and Lillian, from the collection of Edith's belongings which Elizabeth Wilkins put aside for them. Today the pages of the diary reside at the Imperial War Museum in London. The pages evidence Edith's involvement with the escape network and of her continuing enthusiasm for the work. On 27th April 1915, for example, she wrote:

'…People are wonderfully generous with their with their loyal help – I went to a new house and there secured the services of a man who comes to take our guests of Café Oviers to safe houses and where they can abide till it is time for departure. A little widow with a big house gives shelter to some & does all the work without a servant, waiting on and cooking for them with the best courage & good will in the world.'

From time to time Germans would arrive unexpectedly to search the Clinique. Everyone knew that to harbour escaped enemy soldiers was a capital offence. Among the fugitives, in the early Spring of 1915, was one Captain, later Géneral Giraud, of the French Army, who had been captured in the Battle of Guise in August 1914 but escaped two months later. Giraud was captured again by the Germans during Second World War, but with the help of the Allied secret service he escaped from Koenigstein Castle and went on to become civil and military chief of French North Africa.

Things at the Clinique were made more risky by the irresponsible behaviour of a few of the escapees. Although she was aware that her buildings were being watched, Edith believed the fugitives she was harbouring needed fresh air and exercise and thus she allowed the men to go out. However, some of them would get drunk whenever possible and were not

La Libre Belgique (The Free Belgian): Underground newspaper featuring a faked photo of General von Bissing reading the paper, 1915

above raising suspicions with a noisy rendition of the British marching song: 'It's a long way to Tipperary'. Nevertheless, the flow of escaped soldiers continued. And so did the visits of the secret police—the Geheime Politische Polizei during one of which Edith's assistant destroyed the records she kept in her desk—much to Edith's distress.

Chapter 8. Arrest, trial and execution

In June Princesse Marie de Croÿ called to tell Edith to stop: the Chateau de Bellignies had been searched. She recalled:

'Miss Cavell was attending to an operation upstairs. So I waited in her sitting-room until a big dog bounded in, followed by his mistress. She was slight but very straight, with, with large earnest grey eyes which seemed to see through one and a manner which commanded respect.'

Edith told her that she knew she was suspected and that she was under observation by a gang of 'workmen' digging up the road opposite, but noticeably doing no digging. She told the Princess that the Berkendael had been searched the previous day, telling her 'I had only time to throw my papers in the grate, pour alcohol over them, and set them alight, when the Germans came in and began searching the room.' The Princess saw relief come over Edith's face when they talked about stopping, but on hearing there were still thirty men hidden in Cambrai, she said they could not give up: 'because, if one got caught and shot, it would be our fault.'

That month saw a visit to the Clinique by Otto Mayer, of the secret police at a time when there were four French and Belgian soldiers in the wards. Only quick thinking by the Sister in Charge, Elizabeth Wilkins, avoided their being detected. The German

Philippe Baucq

governor of Brussels, General Luttwitz, issued her with strict instructions about the reporting of any British wounded. Police raids continued at the rate of about one a week. Sensing that she would soon be arrested, Edith began to dispose of evidence that could be used against her – hiding documents at the Café de l'Océan, which stood near to the Clinique. On 29th July George Gaston Quien, a Frenchman, was refused admittance to the Clinique after telling Edith a story she did not believe about his being in the service of French Intelligence. Quien certainly misrepresented himself and is today considered to have been an informant for the German secret police. On 31st July, the Germans arrested one of the members of the escape network, the architect Phillipe Baucq. On 5th August Edith herself was arrested, together with Sister Wilkins. Edith's office was searched and left in a sorry state. Elizabeth Wilkins was separately interrogated but was released after her interrogators concluded that she had been kept in ignorance of the details of the escape network. The day after her arrest Edith was permitted to write to Grace Jemmett. She told Grace not to worry and to tell her dog, Jack, she would be back soon. After 72 hours questioning, the German interrogators played a trick. They told Edith that they already had the necessary information and that she could only save her friends from execution, if she made a full confession. So she told them what she thought they already knew, including with, some naïveté, the names of key members of the escape system including that of Prince Reginald de Croÿ. To her first statement, made on 8th August she later added two more, incriminating even more colleagues, although there is some question as to the truthfulness of the statements which she is supposed to have signed. Her statements were made in French and subsequently translated into German and it was the German versions that she signed. Whilst she had linguistic talent, she was not a practiced German speaker and it seems that elements of them were manipulated – this was commented upon by Edith's fellow accused, including Louise Thuliez and Georges Hostelet. Trial documents published after the War by Ambrose Got imply that the Germans had also secured confessions from Mlle. Thuliez, Philippe Baucq, the Comptess de Belleville, Louis Séverin, Madame Bodart, Hermann Capiau, Albert Libiez, Georges Derveau, Princess Marie de Croÿ, Louise Ladière, Georges Hostelet, Constant Cayron, Armand Heuze and twelve others.

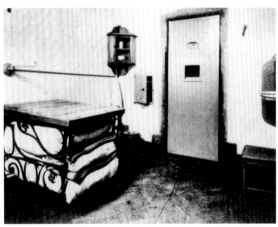

Edith Cavell's cell in St. Gilles prison as it was preserved after the War

On 10th August she was transferred from the police headquarters to St. Gilles Prison. She was soon joined by other members of the escape network. They were to find themselves accused of war treason. Edith's cell at St. Gilles was small and gloomy with just a small window, too high to allow her a view. In her prison cell she had with her a copy of *The Imitation of Christ*, a devotional work by Thomas à Kempis (c.1380 – 1471), a German Catholic monk and she read the book regularly, marking passages which struck her particularly. She worked on embroidery, making table mats which are preserved in the Imperial War Museum in London. She was sent flowers by her nurses and allowed to write to them, saying: 'In everything one can learn new lessons of life, and if you were in my place you would realise how precious liberty is, and would certainly undertake never to abuse it.'

On 23rd August she was able to write to Sister Wilkins. She was concerned about the welfare of Grace Jemmett, whose private patient fees had fallen into arrears because Grace's father in England had been unable to communicate with the Berkendael. Edith sent money for her immediate needs and hoped that M. Heger would allow her to stay as: 'otherwise I cannot see what will become of her.' She was also solicitous for the welfare of the Berkendael's remaining staff, particularly the domestic staff and that the nurses studied regularly for their exams.

Back in England, Edith's brother-in-law, Dr Longworth Wainwright wrote to the Foreign Office on August 24, 1915: 'I have news through Dutch sources that my wife's sister, a Miss Edith Cavell, has been arrested in Brussels and can get no news of what has happened to her since August 5.' In September she was allowed some contact with officials from the American Legation in Brussels. She informed the American officials that she had admitted hiding English and French soldiers in her house and they undertook to try to see that she got a fair trial.

On 3rd October, seventeen nurses of the Belgian School for Trained Nurses petitioned the German Governor-General in Brussels, Baron von Bissing, on Edith's behalf, reminding him of her eight years of self sacrificing work at the Clinique. The petition was carefully worded and was possibly drafted by the German speaking father of one of the signatories, Germaine van Aerschodt.

Prison de St-Gilles

Mes chères Nurses

C'est un moment très triste pour moi quand je vous écris pour vous faire mes adieux. Il me faut rappeler que le 17 Septembre a vu la fin des huit ans de ma direction de l'Ecole. J'étais si heureuse d'être appelée à aider dans l'organisation de l'œuvre que notre comité venait de fonder. Le 1er Oct. de l'année 1907 il n'y avait que 4 jeunes élèves, maintenant vous êtes déjà nombreuses, en tout entre 50 et 60, je pense, comptant celles qui sont diplomées et qui ont quitté l'Ecole.

Je vous ai raconté à différentes reprises ces premiers jours et les difficultés que nous avons rencontré, jusque dans le choix des mots pour vos heures "de service" et "hors de service" été ; tout était nouveau dans la profession pour la Belgique.

Peu à peu un service après l'autre a été établi - les infirmières diplomées pour soigner dans les maisons particulières - les infirmières scolaires -

Letter from Edith Cavell to her nurses, 10th October 1915

Nevertheless, Edith's Court Martial, before a military tribunal, began on 7th October 1915. The inhabitants of Brussels were apprehensive about the trial, which was held in the Senate Building in the Rue de la Loi, Brussels. It attracted a large audience with many German officers in attendance. Five German judges, all German officers, heard the case. The prosecution was led by Dr. Eduard Stoeber, an ambitious lawyer from Bavaria, who was to dominate the trial proceedings. Arrested whilst wearing her matron's uniform, Edith sent word to Sister Wilkins to send civilian clothes for her to wear at her trial.

It has been conjectured that she might have created a better impression with the court had she worn her nursing uniform. When she saw her wearing civilian clothes in at the Court Martial, it was the first time that Marie de Croÿ had seen her out of her Matron's uniform. Clara Bohme told the biographer Rowland Ryder that it was not Miss Cavell's practice to wear uniform outside the Clinique, but other sources suggest she wore it when travelling and in some informal situations. Until the First World War it was not considered unusual for nurses to wear uniform off duty – both in England and in Brussels. Perhaps she was trying to separate her role in the escape network from her image as a professional nurse or she may have thought that by wearing uniform she could be seen as trying unfairly to win favour with her military judges.

The court martial read depositions attributed to the accused. According to Ambroise Gott, Edith's deposition included the lines:

'I provided lodging for the Englishmen because they were in peril of their lives. I suppose this to be the case with all former English soldiers, who are in Belgium. Through my mediation some 200 men have been directed as far as the frontier'.

She was the first of the accused to be interrogated at the trial. One of her judges, Freiherr von Cornberg noted Edith's 'tall, haggard appearance, cold face in which no excitement is to be seen.' An American diplomatic official, Hugh Gibson, who was present at the trial felt that she 'spoke without trembling and showed a clear mind.' He recorded: 'When she was asked why she helped these soldiers to go to England, she replied that she thought that, if she had not done so, they would have been shot by the Germans, and that therefore she thought she only did her duty to her country in saving their lives.' Under cross examination by Dr Stoeber, she was asked who was the head of the organisation: she replied that it didn't have one. Asked about the role of her fellow accused, Philippe Baucq, she said she knew him very little. Dr Stoeber put to her that in 'recruiting' men her actions favoured Germany's enemies. She responded: 'My preoccupation has not been to aid the enemy but to help the men who applied to me to reach the frontier; once across the frontier they were free.'

On 9th October the judgement of the Court Martial was passed in secret. Edith Cavell, along with Phillipe Baucq, Louise Thuliez, Louis Séverin and Countess Jeanne de Belleville were condemned to death. The Princesse de Croÿ, Herman Capiau, Albert Libiez and two others got ten years hard labour and seventeen others were sentenced to terms of imprisonment varying from two to eight years. The grounds for the judgement asserted that Miss Cavell was one of the chief organisers of the escape network. The Governor, General von Sauberzweig ordered an immediate execution of the death sentence against Phillipe Baucq and Edith Cavell, setting the date and time as 07.00 on 12th October. He adjourned the death sentence on the other prisoners until appeals for clemency could be heard. The judgement was not made known to the condemned until 11th October. Edith heard the news from Pastor le Seur. She refused to appeal for clemency, conjecturing that such an appeal would be unlikely to succeed. She had already written a last letter to her nurses, reminding them of her pride in the achievements of the school and the 56 nurses who had trained there over the past eight years and confided that despite appearances she had loved them all more than they knew. She advised them that 'devotion will bring you true happiness'.

That same evening she received a visit from her friend The Reverend Stirling Gahan who recorded her last words:

'I have no fear nor shrinking, I have seen death so often that it is not strange or fearful to me… life has always been hurried and full of difficulty. This time of rest has been a great mercy. Everyone here has been very kind. This I would say, standing as I do in view of God and Eternity, I realize that patriotism is not enough. I must have no hatred or bitterness towards anyone.'

She received Holy Communion in her cell. Her final message was written to her friend (and patient) Grace Jemmett included the lines:

'My dear girl, how shall I write to you this last day? … Nothing matters when one comes to the last hour but a clear conscience, and life looks so wasted and full of wrong-doing and things left undone… I want you to go to England at once now and ask Dr. Wainwright to put you where you can be cured. Don't mind how hard it is. Do it for my sake and then try to find something useful to do, something to make you forget yourself while making others happy. If God permits I will watch over you and wait for you on the other side. Be sure to get ready for then. I want you to know that I am neither afraid, nor unhappy, but quite ready to give my life for England.'

Grace returned to England with Sister Elizabeth Wilkins in November 1915.

On the morning of October 12th 1915 Edith Cavell was driven by car from the Prison of St. Gilles to the rifle range at the Tir National, which had been pressed into service as an execution ground for prisoners at St Gilles prison who had been condemned to death. She was led to the execution post by Pastor le Seur and blindfolded. Phillipe Baucq, who was to be executed alongside Edith refused a blindfold: she did not. In accordance with the sentence, at 7 o'clock the firing squad opened fire. Three bullets entered Edith's chest, a fourth went into her forehead. She died instantly. The doctor who pronounced her dead, Gottfried Benn, latter recalled that she met her end with poise and dignity. Her body was interred in a simple grave at the execution ground.

On the flyleaf of her copy of *The Imitation of Christ* are inscribed the dates of her arrest, imprisonment and court martial. These are followed by the words: 'Died at 7a.m. on October 12th 1915. E. Cavell With love to E.D. Cavell' Similar words are inscribed in her copy of and The Book of Common Prayer. The handwriting in the former is very similar to Edith's cursive hand and one can only assume that she was therefore permitted to write these words shortly before her death, in the knowledge of the time of her execution. The inscription in her prayer book is formally written and probably not Edith's own. That she wanted these very personal belongings to go to her cousin Eddy is clear - she retained a fondness for him throughout her life – and he duly received *The Imitation of Christ* and had it published as a special Edith Cavell edition of the work. Eddy Cavell never married and died in 1945.

The written statements which she signed giving detailed evidence which could be used against her colleagues, telling how she had hidden men in the clinic, have brought a measure of condemnation from some of Edith Cavell's biographers. German Wartime propaganda suggested that she alone signed statements, but the evidence presented by Ambroise Got, a French journalist who claimed to have obtained the principal trial documents from 'a German political personage' suggests otherwise. One of her annotations on the flyleaf of *The Imitation of Christ* relates to the number of accused who were present at the court martial in the Salle des Deputés. It reads: 'the accused numbered in all 70 of whom 34 were present on these two dates' (7 – 8 October 1915). The implication is that 36 of the accused were released from St. Gilles prison without charge. Perhaps she was hinting that the statements she had signed, by implicating some might have helped to get others released. It seems likely that she believed all the accused would escape the death penalty and be sentenced, at worst, to terms of imprisonment. In that respect at least her statements can be seen as naïve, but it seems harsh to criticise someone so dedicated to public service, so used to fair dealing and to inspiring high standards of practice in others for showing a lack of understanding of the politics of War. The Princess Marie de Croÿ who with her husband Prince Reginald was at the centre of the escape network, later recorded this assessment of Edith Cavell's character:

'She was an earnest Christian and acted from a sense of humanity and duty. I do not think she did not care if she lived. She took every precaution for herself and for me, but duty came first, and she was too puritanically truthful to be able to defend herself.'

Mlle. Bihet, Director of the Intitut Edith Cavell – Marie Depage, Brussels reflecting on her predecessor wrote:

'She said that her time in prison had been such a rest for her. I think that was true. Of course I did not know her but I think I have a feeling about what she much have been through. I would not be surprised that she had to endure so much that she felt life was not worthwhile to fight for it, especially if to escape the Germans' enquiry she had to lie. That was so contrary to her puritan conscience.'

What is clear is that the number people she helped to escape from occupied Belgium far exceeded the 250 or so she admitted to in her depositions and that the real figure is closer to a thousand.

Chapter 9. Aftermath

Diplomatic efforts on behalf of Edith Cavell led by Brand Whitlock, the United States Ambassador in Brussels, had been going for several weeks and involved Spanish, Belgian, French and English diplomats. The worldwide reaction to Miss Cavell's execution was not what the German authorities had been expecting and was overwhelmingly hostile. At a time when America was neutral, it was seen by many in the United States as an act of wanton cruelty. In allied countries, particularly in Britain, it was soon taken up by propagandists. Posters. postcards and other memorabilia featuring portraits of Miss Cavell and melodramatic and inaccurate depictions of her execution were soon in circulation. Kaiser Wilhelm II let it be known that executions of women should not proceed in future without his consent. In Brussels the death sentences on the Comtesse de Belleville, Louise Thuliez and Louis Séverin were commuted to terms of imprisonment. In the British Parliament, the Prime Minister, Herbert Asquith, made a speech extolling the virtues of Edith Cavell and decrying her execution and her story, often misinterpreted, remained a potent propaganda weapon for the remainder of the War. Sir Horace Rowland, senior diplomat at the Foreign Office wrote privately to his colleagues: 'I had hoped that the Germans wouldn't go beyond imprisoning her in Germany. Their action in this matter is part and parcel of their policy of frightfulness and also I venture to think a sign of weakness.'

After the war, in 1919, her body was disinterred and brought back on a British warship for a burial service in Westminster Abbey which had some of the trappings of a state funeral. Her remains were then

Edith Cavell's funeral procession, Embankment, London, 1919

taken to be buried in the shade of Norwich Cathedral. At her old hospital, The London, a nurses' home, whose construction costs were supported by a national collection, was named the Edith Cavell Home at the personal request of Queen Alexandra. In 1920 Miss Cavell's statue at St. Martin's Place, which was intended to be a national monument to nurses was unveiled by Queen Alexandra. Ever since then nurses from what is now The Royal London Hospital, have laid a wreath at its base on the anniversary of her execution. In Brussels, the new site of what became as the Institut Edith Cavell- Marie Depage in the Uccle district was completed in 1926. Her

London Hospital sisters laying a wreath at the statue of Edith Cavell, St Martin's Place, London, 1960s

character was recreated in film by actresses Sybil Thorndyke (in Dawn, 1928) and by Anna Neagle (in Nurse Edith Cavell, 1939), both films being made by Herbert Wilcox. More recently, Joan Plowright played her in a play entitled 'Cavell'.

It has been argued that she somehow sought martyrdom, but Edith's words to a colleague during her trial: 'what does it matter as long as we're not shot' would seem to prove otherwise. She is still revered by her fellow nurses, by people in her native county of Norfolk, in her adopted country of Belgium and by a great many others around the world. Above all, people are struck by her words especially by the words inscribed on her statue in London:

Patriotism is not enough – I must have no hatred or bitterness for anyone.

References

Berkeley, Reginald (1928) *Dawn: a biographical novel of Edith Cavell.* Sears, New York

Bingham, Stella (1979) *Ministering Angels.* Osprey, London

Boston, Noel (1976) *The Dutiful Edith Cavell.* Norwich Cathedral.

Bridges, Daisy Caroline (1967): *A History of the International Council of Nurses 189 – 1964.* London, Pitman Medical

Brown, Gordon (2007) *Courage: Eight Portraits.* Bloomsbury, London

Burdett, Henry, Kt. (1899): *Burdett's Official Nursing Directory*

Census for England and Wales, 1861, 1871, 1881, 1891, 1901

Clark-Kennedy, A E (1965) Edith Cavell: *Pioneer and Patriot.* London, Faber

Daunton, Claire, ed. (1990) *Edith Cavell: Her Life and Her Art.* Royal London Hospital

De Leeuw, Adele (1968) *Edith Cavell: Nurse, Spy, Heroine.* Putnam

Elkon, Juliette (1956) *Edith Cavell: Heroic Nurse.* Messner

Fitzgerald, Alice (1917) *The Edith Cavell Nurse from Massachusetts.* A record of one year's personal service with the British Expeditionary Force in France, Boulogne, *The Somme 1916-1917 with an account of the imprisonment, trial and death of Edith Cavell.* Boston, Butterfield

Gordon, J. Elsie (1976) *Edith Cavell – Pioneer Nurse and Wartime Martyr* (in *Midwife, Health Visitor & Community Nurse*, vol. 12)

Grey, Elizabeth (1916) *Friend within the Gates: The Story of Edith Cavell.* Houghton

Mifflin Hales, Irene (1984) *Maidstone's Typhoid Epidemic* (in *Bygone Kent*, vol. 5, no. 4)

Hoehling, Adolf A. (1957) *A Whisper of Eternity; The Mystery of Edith Cavell.* Yoseloff, New York

Johns, Rowland, ed. (1934) *Nurse Cavell, Dog Lover.* Methuen

Judson, Helen (1941) *Edith Cavell.* Macmillan

Leeds, Herbert (1915) *Edith Cavell: The Story of Her Life.* London, Jarrold

McFadyen, Phillip (1983) *Edith Cavell 1865-1915, a Norfolk Heroine.* Swardeston Parochial Church Council. 3rd edition.

McGann, Susan (1992) *The battle of the Nurses: a Study of Eight Women Who Influenced the Development of Professional Nursing, 1880 – 1930.* Scutari Press, London

Norton-Taylor, Richard: *'How British Diplomats Failed Edith Cavell'* (article published in *The Guardian*, 12 October 2005)

Protheroe, Ernest (1918) *A Noble Woman: The life of Edith Cavell.* Epworth, London

Richardson, Nigel (1986) *Edith Cavell.* David and Charles

Rivett, Geoffrey (1986) *The Development of the London Hospital System 1823 – 1982.* King's Fund, London

Ryder, Rowland (1975) *Edith Cavell.* Hamilton, London

Skene, K.V. (2004) *Edith Louise Cavell December 4 1865-October 12 1915.*

Vinton, Iris (1959) *The Story of Edith Cavell.* Grosset & Dunlap

Waterer, Lillian *Memories of Miss Cavell.* Originally published in *The London Hospital League of Nurses Review.*

White, Kathleen (1985) *Edith Cavell.* Marshall Pickering, London

The Women Who Made Our City What it is Today (article published in *Peterborough Evening Telegraph*, 24 August 2004)

Archival Sources

Photographic copy of application of Edith Cavell to Fountain Fever Hospital, 6th December 1895 (Royal London Hospital biographical collection ref: LH/Z/1/CAVELL)

References in support of Edith Cavell's application to be a Regular probationer at the London Hospital, 1896 (Royal London Hospital Archives ref: LH/N/7/7/30).

London Hospital register of probationers no 5, 1894 - 1897 (Royal London Hospital Archives ref: LH/N/1/5)

London Hospital Private Nursing Institution register no. 4, 1898 - 1899 (Royal London Hospital Archives ref:LH/N/5/4)

London Hospital register sisters and nurses, no. 1, 1880 - 1903 (Royal London Hospital Archives ref: RLHLH/N/4/1)

Eva C.E. Lückes: personal correspondence with Florence Nightingale 1889 -

1898 (Royal London Hospital Archives ref: RLHPP/LUC/1)

Eva C.E. Lückes: *Matron's annual letter* 1907 - 1915 (Royal London Hospital Archives ref: LH/N/7/1/14-212)

Letters from Edith Cavell to Eva Lückes, 1902 - 1913 (Royal London Hospital Archives ref: LH/N/7/7/1-21)

Draft of a letter from Edith Cavell to unnamed patient returning gift to Nurse Birch, 5 July 1909 (Royal London Hospital Archives ref: LH/N/7/7/22)

The Hospital: a journal of the medical sciences and hospital management and administration, 5 (July 1909), 126 – 127. Editor's marked copies (Royal London Hospital Archives)

Manuscript notes by Edith Cavell appealing to women to take up nursing as a profession, c. 1909 (Royal London Hospital Archives ref: RLHCI/1/2)

Letter by Dr Longworth Wainwright concerning the fate of Edith Cavell, 24.8.1915 and internal memo by Sir Horace Rowland (National Archives ref: FO 383/15).

Typescript quotations about Edith Cavell, by Princess de Croÿ and Mlle M. Bihet (Royal London Hospital Archives ref: LH/Z/1/CAVELL)

Crispin, Margaret E. M/s lecture on Edith Cavell, 1992 (Royal London Hospital ref: LH/Z/1/CAVELL)

ALAN BRERETON
WATFORD GENERAL HOSPITAL
LETCHMORE WARD
SIDE ROOM 2
VICARRE ROAD
 2 D1   1 80 HB.
       2D18 OHB

54